6 TOP TRUMPS

CARDS

OPTIMUS PRIME

Optimus Prime has spent years in hiding as Earth turns against him. But when a new power threatens humanity itself, he must find new faith in mankind.

TOP TRUMPS FILE

SIZE: 30
STRENGTH: 26
TERROR: 5
SPEED: 10
DISGUISE: 8

FREE & EXCLUSIVE

CONTENTS

7	IN THE BEGINNING
8	INTRODUCING THE AUTOBOTS
10	FACT FILE: OPTIMUS PRIME
11	CADE'S WORDSEARCH
12	ROBOTS IN DISGUISE
13	TRANSFORMERS 4 POSTER
14	FROM THE DARK SIDE
16	TRANSFORMERS 4 STORY
24	WHEN DINOBOTS RULED THE EARTH!
26	FACT FILE: GALVATRON
27	FACT FILE: GRIMLOCK
28	PRIME NUMBER
29	AGE OF EXTINCTION
30	LOCKDOWN'S LOWDOWN
32	BOTROBS IN GISSUIDE
33	FRIEND OR FOE?
34	SHOCKWAVE'S SHOCK AND AWE! PART 1
36	RATCHET'S RIDDLES
38	PRIME TIME
40	TRANSFORMERS 3 POSTER
41	CLASH OF THE TITANS!
42	FACT FILE: BUMBLEBEE
43	PRIME OBJECTIVE!
44	TRANSFORMERS 3 STORY
48	SHOCKWAVE'S SHOCK AND AWE! PART 2
50	WHICH TRANSFORMER ARE YOU?
52	TRANSFORMERS 2 POSTER
53	COUNTDOWN
54	MEGATRON'S MASTERPLAN
55	REAL OR FAKE?
56	TRANSFORMERS 2 STORY
60	FIGHT TO THE DEATH!
62	CREATE YOUR OWN AUTOBOT AND DECEPTICON MASKS!
64	TRANSFORMERS 1 POSTER
65	CREATE YOUR OWN TRANSFORMER
66	MORE THAN MEETS THE EYE!
68	TRANSFORMERS 1 STORY
72	DRAW BUMBLEBEE
74	FACT FILE: RATCHET
75	JOIN THE DOTS
76	ANSWERS

In The Beginning

Millions of years ago, the metallic planet Cybertron floated majestically like a silver star through the outer reaches of space. Inhabited entirely by a population of robots with a technology level far more advanced than 21st century Earth, life on Cybertron should have been heavenly. Sadly, it was anything but. It quickly descended into a dangerous and violent battleground.

A brutal civil war soon erupted between two factions of robots. The Autobots, led by heroic and honourable Optimus Prime, are a force for good. However, their enemies the Decepticons are the exact opposite: scheming, deceitful and untrustworthy. Conflict between the two sides raged for years, tragically destroying Cybertron in the process. But the end of Cybertron did not mark the end of the war. Now both sides have brought their struggle to a new home, our own planet: Earth.

Continuing their fight on Earth, both the Autobots and Decepticons have the ability to disguise themselves as cars, planes, trucks and other vehicles, allowing them to blend seamlessly into their new surroundings.

This ability to change has led them to become know as....

THE TRANSFORMERS

INTRODUCING THE AUTOBOTS

Optimus Prime: Heroic leader of the Autobots.

Bumblebee: Information gatherer. Closer to humans than most.

Ratchet: Medical Officer. Dedicated to saving and preserving lives at any cost.

With the Transformers' war now being waged on our own planet, it has never been more important to identify who is good and who is bad. These are the Autobots. Locked in a seemingly eternal struggle with the evil Decepticons dating back thousands of years. The Autobots can be relied upon to defend the causes of freedom and liberty. They try to avoid harming humans or anything on their adopted planet as much as possible. The key Autobots are pictured below:

Crosshairs:
Paratrooper. Armourer and weapons master, a loyal ally in battle but often very cautious.

Drift:
Adept at devising plans, a legacy of his past as an ex-Decepticon Samurai warrior.

OPTIMUS PRIME

Huge, majestic and all powerful, few Transformers are as widely respected and feared as Optimus Prime, the leader of the Autobots. Admired by both sides, Prime's status has not come easily. He has led the Autobots through many challenges, helping them escape their doomed home planet of Cybertron and ultimately defeating Megatron, the leader of the Decepticons.

Although he is wise, he's not content to stand on the sidelines barking orders in a battle situation. The Autobot leader has the ability to change himself into a truck, of the sort, commonly seen on his adopted home Earth. He is a formidable warrior in combat and both his friends and enemies look up to him all the more for that.

AFFILIATION:	**AUTOBOT**
JOB TITLE:	**LEADER**
ALT MODE:	**TRUCK**
PRIMARY WEAPON:	**SWORD**

IN SUMMARY: Wise, decent and good but also a formidable enemy in battle.

CADE'S WORDSEARCH

Y	T	L	A	O	O	S	M	D	F	E	C	G	Z
T	P	O	B	U	M	B	L	E	B	E	E	R	H
T	U	C	N	J	X	E	X	C	R	V	U	V	F
D	T	K	C	R	O	S	S	H	A	I	R	S	Q
Z	Q	D	C	Y	C	L	O	N	U	S	V	H	I
L	M	O	G	A	L	V	A	T	R	O	N	E	R
V	Y	W	V	K	F	O	H	D	U	F	V	N	S
G	I	N	W	M	G	N	O	I	F	E	I	R	T
R	R	O	P	T	I	M	U	S	P	R	I	M	E
I	A	L	R	I	O	P	N	S	O	V	W	D	D
M	T	R	E	D	S	D	D	M	M	A	R	R	N
L	C	S	T	I	N	G	E	R	P	E	X	I	O
O	H	Y	M	R	W	L	U	A	R	L	Q	F	T
C	E	I	N	I	O	E	O	B	A	J	S	T	E
K	T	G	O	H	I	I	R	M	V	A	C	R	T

Poor Cade Yeager! Until recently he was enjoying a simple life and knew nothing of the ways of Autobots and Decepticons. Help him to improve his knowledge of the world of Transformers by locating as many of the Transformers listed in the wordsearch to the left.

BUMBLEBEE
CROSSHAIRS
CYCLONUS
DRIFT
GALVATRON
GRIMLOCK
HOUND
LOCKDOWN
OPTIMUS
PRIME
RATCHET
STINGER

ROBOTS IN DISGUISE

For all their differences, both Autobots and Decepticons have one thing in common: neither would last long without their ability to metamorphose into man-made vehicles such as cars and lorries. This tactic ensures that they can remain disguised from their potential enemies on Earth and lay low if they need to.

But which Transformers change into what? Identify these Transformers below from these pictures of them in their non-robotic camouflage.

1:

2:

3:

4:

5:

6:

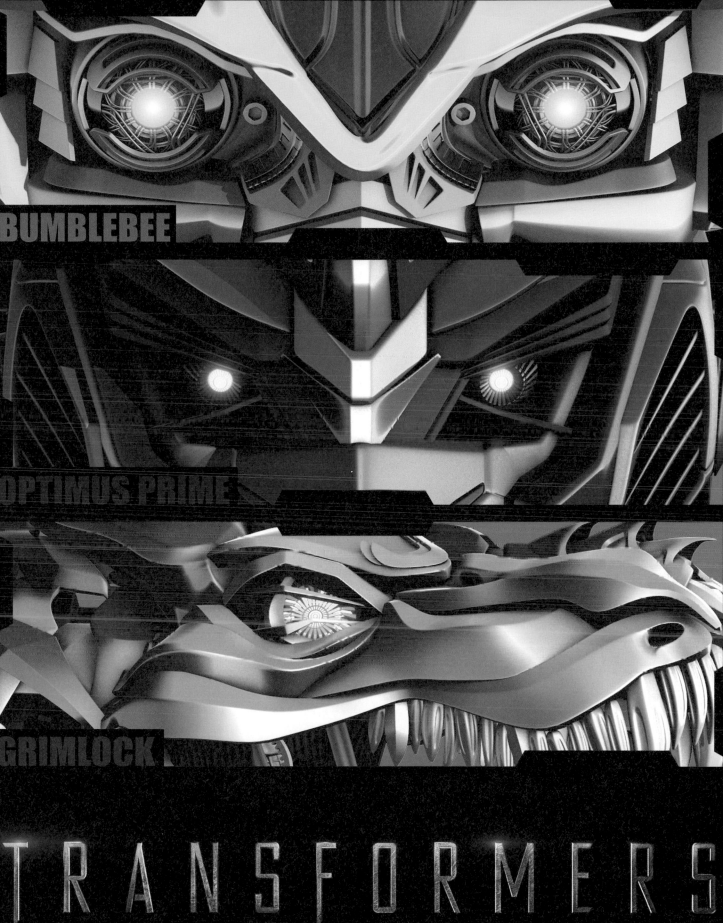

BUMBLEBEE

OPTIMUS PRIME

GRIMLOCK

TRANSFORMERS

From the dark side...

The exact opposite of the heroic Autobots in almost every way, the Decepticons are evil, malevolent and hell bent on domination of not only the world but the entire galaxy. Naturally, they hate all Autobots just as the Autobots dislike them. But, unlike the Autobots, they care nothing for Earth and will think nothing of destroying human civilisation to achieve their dastardly aims. Do not trust them!

Galvatron:
This formidable prototype offers both the best and worst of both worlds. On the plus side, his physical frame is closely modelled on the finest Autobot of them all: Optimus Prime. But this counts for little as his mind and spirit contain the essence of Prime's mortal enemy, the dead Decepticon leader Megatron!

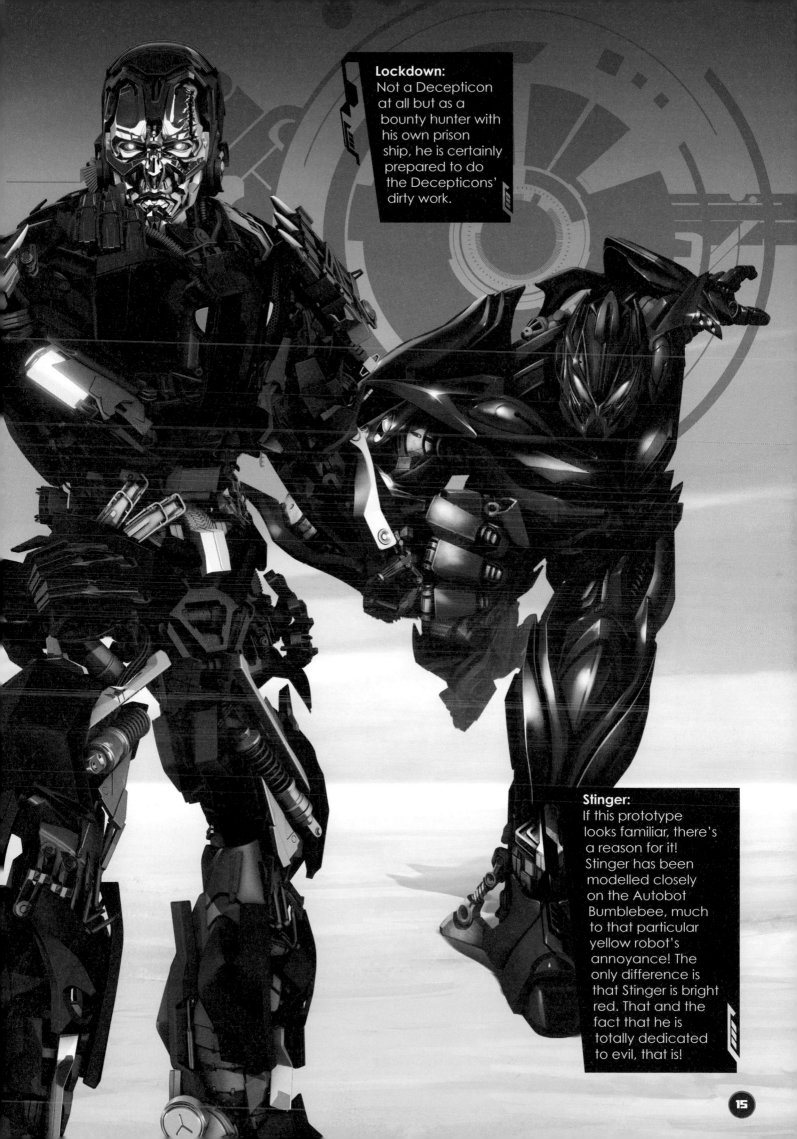

Lockdown:
Not a Decepticon at all but as a bounty hunter with his own prison ship, he is certainly prepared to do the Decepticons' dirty work.

Stinger:
If this prototype looks familiar, there's a reason for it! Stinger has been modelled closely on the Autobot Bumblebee, much to that particular yellow robot's annoyance! The only difference is that Stinger is bright red. That and the fact that he is totally dedicated to evil, that is!

TRANSFORMERS
AGE OF EXTINCTION

Earth. Sixty-five million years ago. A small dinosaur looks up to see a large shiny object travelling through the sky. The dinosaur, of course, has no idea what the spaceship is or what its actions mean. But within seconds, the craft has unleashed a seed which on hitting the ground begins to coat not just the dinosaur but the entire world with layers of metal. For the dinosaurs, the Age of Extinction has begun… Much later, in the present day, Earth's human population is still recovering from the devastating Decepticon attacks of a few years before. The city of Chicago has by now been almost totally rebuilt.

The government is using ex-military men like Harold Attinger, the head of the Savoy Strike team to hunt down Decepticons. In fact, Attinger secretly hates ALL Transformers, both Autobot and Decepticon. In Alaska, a young British scientist Darcy Tirrell is puzzled by a remarkable discovery: a dinosaur fossil that is entirely metallic black. What could this mean?

Meanwhile, at an industrial port, the Savoy Strike assault team track down the Autobot Ratchet who has received an alarming message from Autobot leader, Optimus Prime. "Autobots, we are under targeted attack," the message began. "Initiate shadow protocol. Cease all contact with the humans."

Suddenly, a large robotic figure, Lockdown, emerges from the water. Neither Autobot nor Decepticon, he is a bounty hunter working with Savoy, to hunt down all Transformers. He immediately confronts Ratchet. "Where is Optimus Prime?" he asks, shooting at him, but Ratchet bravely refuses to tell him where his friend is. Sadly, this act of resistance proves to be the last thing Ratchet ever does. Lockdown kills Ratchet, extracts his spark, switches into a car and drives off.

All of these events seem very distant from the life of Cade Yeager, a wannabe inventor, hopeless with money, who lives with his teenage daughter Tessa in the American state of Texas. Tessa often gets fed up with her father and is particularly cross when one day she sees that he has bought an apparently useless grey truck on his latest outing with his old friend Lucas. The Yeager Farmhouse is already full of junk, much of it the result of Cade's failed attempts to invent things. Tessa also doubts that she'll be able to afford to go to college. Will she be trapped here forever? Cade, however, is keen that his daughter should not repeat the mistakes that he made in his early life. She must finish school and should not go out with any boys until she is older, he says.

Cade decides to clean the old truck which he could see quickly was quite badly damaged. On activating the radio, however, he hears a "Calling All Autobots!" signal. The truck is clearly a Transformer! Tessa points out that the government are offering money for any Transformers found: money which they could really do with.

But Cade, being Cade, is naturally curious and pulls a bit of shrapnel out of the truck's engine. It turns out to be an unexploded missile! The Yeagers are very lucky not to be blown sky high.

Removing the missile does at least wake the Transformer up. He soon reveals himself to be Autobot leader Optimus Prime. He makes it clear that he needs to contact the other Autobots immediately.

Meanwhile, Savoy boss Harold Attinger has met with the bounty hunter Lockdown in the jungle. Lockdown has brought a huge Prison Ship with him from space. He tells Attinger that he has no real loyalty to anyone other than himself. Back in Texas, Cade has sent his friend Lucas to the nearest shop to get some spare parts.
On the way, Lucas sees a sign offering a $250,000 reward for information on vehicles which could secretly be Transformers. Lucas thinks of the truck Cade bought, thinks about the money and calls the number on the poster, getting through to Harold Attinger himself almost straight away.

Lucas's greed soon caused huge problems for the Yeagers. From Lucas's description, Attinger recognises the truck as Optimus Prime. He orders "Operation: Cemetery Wind" to scramble. Soon Attinger, Lockdown and the Savoy Strike team have raided the Yeager Farmhouse. Attinger begins shouting at Tessa, demanding to know more about the truck.

Optimus is soon doing battle with Lockdown outside the farmhouse. In the course of the battle, Cade's friend Lucas is killed when a grenade Lockdown throws turns him into metal.

Tess and Cade run for their lives. They soon encounter a young man in a car who turns out to be Tessa's boyfriend, Shane. Cade is not pleased to find out Tessa is going out with someone, especially after he had urged her not to. On the other hand, he is relieved Shane turns out to be an amazing driver who helps them to escape. They go into hiding and meet up with several other Autobots: Bumblebee, Drift, Hound and Crosshairs. Bumblebee had led the group in Prime's absence.

Meanwhile, in Chicago, important scientific work is being carried out by a company called KSI (Kinetic Solutions Inc). Joshua Jones, the head of the company, working with the British scientist Darcy Tirrell, has been gathering a substance called Transformium from remains left behind from the attack on Chicago. Transformium can be turned into anything. The KSI also plug wires into the heads of the dead Transformers Megatron and Sentinel Prime to retrieve information from their brains. Joshua plans to build his own Transformers using this information in a factory in China.

Thanks to Cade's hacking, the Autobots soon finds out about the KSI. They travel to Chicago and sneak into their headquarters. Bumblebee is enraged to find a red Transformer closely modelled on himself called Stinger inside the lab. Another prototype called Galvatron looks very much like Optimus Prime and is clearly modelled on him.

"We can make you now, don't you get it?" sneers Joshua Jones on entering and seeing Optimus Prime. "We don't need you anymore!"

The scientist proceeds to activate Galvatron, Stinger and another prototype. All of these three quickly hypo-transform: splintering apart before reforming in their new disguises, something the usual Transformers could never do.

"You're not one of us!" shouts Optimus, fighting the prototype robots. "You never will be. For you have no soul!"

"And that is why I have no fear!" responds Galvatron. Joshua is puzzled by Galvatron's words. He has never programmed the prototypes to talk!

Soon Lockdown has captured both Tessa and Optimus Prime and dragged them onto his prison ship. "Your creators. They want you back. They want to sweep their chessboard clean. They built you to do what you are told," Lockdown tells Prime. There are other imprisoned Transformers on board in the cells, notably a strange bunch who resemble Earth's ancient dinosaurs. Lockdown meanwhile, gives Attinger a seed, like the one which wiped out the dinosaurs. The seed is part of a deal: Attinger had demanded it in exchange for bringing Optimus Prime to Lockdown.

Fighting off various Canine-Bots and Grinder-Bots, Cade and Shane are soon able to blast their way onto the ship, using some stray guns they have found. With Crosshairs' help, they flee onto another ship and escape. In the meantime, Drift and Hound help Optimus escape in a drop ship just as Lockdown's prison ship is about to embark on its journey into space.

Together again, the group realise a few things, namely that Megatron has now transferred his mind into Galvatron's body. This occurred when Megatron's head was wired into the laboratory's machinery. Galvatron now wants the seed Lockdown has given Attinger so that he can metallise an entire city and use the metal to create an army of evil Transformers. That was why the Earth had been metallised in the time of the dinosaurs in the first place: the Creators had used the metal from that to create the first ever Transformers.

With all the problems in Chicago, Joshua decides to order his entire company to move to China. There he plans to detonate the seed in the Mongolian desert, creating enough Transformium to last one hundred years. He plans to then build Transformers from them, profiting from the results. He soon realised Galvatron is after both him and the seed. Bringing his army of prototypes to life, he sneaks off to the nearby island of Hong Kong. But his escape is not sneaky enough! Not only does Galvatron trace him to Hong Kong but so do Harold Attinger and the mercenaries as well as Optimus Prime and the heroes. A big battle ensues as the Autobots crash land in Hong Kong. Fortunately, four other captives had been rescued alongside Prime.

Emerging from the crashed drop ship are the Dinobots! They are twice as big as the Autobots and wield their own maces and clubs. The Dinobots are led by Warpath, who turns into a Tyrannosaurus Rex, followed by Spinosaurus, Triceratops and Swoop, who changes into a two-headed pterodactyl.

Prime speaks to the Dinobots:
"Whatever your crimes are, today they are forgotten. Today you stand with us. Or you stand against me."
They do not respond. Prime becomes unsure of the Dinobots' loyalties and prepares to fight them himself. "We've given you freedom!" he says. "But we cannot restore honour to those who have none. Defend my family. Or die!" Happily, the Dinobots choose to fight alongside Optimus and he and the other Autobots ride on the Dinobots' backs into battle. Warpath belches fire as Prime rides him, the Autobot leader wielding a sword as he does so. "Accept no substitutions!" Bumblebee joked as he fights his near double Stinger while both robots sit on Swoop's back. Bumblebee finally kills Stinger, using the prototype's own sword arm on Stinger himself.

Suddenly, all the robots, including all metal objects, are mysteriously lifted off the ground by some unknown force. Lockdown's prison ship is back and the bounty hunter is blasting everyone with a magnetic field generator. Prime shoots at it and the Transformers all fall to Earth with a bump. But seeing that everyone is distracted, Lockdown seizes the moment to stab Optimus Prime with the Autobot leader's own sword. Thinking fast, Shane pulls the sword out of Prime by attaching it to his car and driving off. Angered, Optimus Prime chops off Lockdown's head.

Soon, the Autobots retreat, flying off using Lockdown's jet packs. Optimus Prime also takes Lockdown's grenades, dropping them onto the prototypes below and thus metallising them, ending their lives forever.

Only Galvatron escapes uttering the words: "We shall meet again Prime. For I exist. And I am free!"

Clearly, the spirit of Megatron will live on to fight another day.

But all is not lost. The Dinobots are now free to roam the Earth, just as the dinosaurs had done millions of years before. Cade also comes to terms with Shane being Tessa's boyfriend.

And Optimus Prime bids the humans farewell, flying off, taking the seeds with him, safe in the knowledge that humanity is once again safe and that order has been restored to the Earth.

WHEN DINOBOTS RULED THE EARTH!

This new metallic species, the Dinobots, have changed from these creatures and become allies with the Autobots', helping them in battle. But who are the Dinobots?

Few more terrifying creatures have ever walked the Earth than the dinosaurs, who last walked the planet 65 million years ago.

Slash:
Sneaky as the day is long, Slash is a terrifying opponent in battle, his name deriving from the lethal cyber scythes he often deploys when in a robot mode. As a Velociraptor, this Dinobot is, if anything, even more deadly.

Grimlock:
Behold Grimlock, leader of the Dinobots! Initially a rival to Optimus Prime, he becomes a key ally of the Autobots. He changes into the king of the Dinosaurs, Tyrannosaurus Rex. ROOOAR!!!

Strafe:
Keep your head down! Strafe changes into a two-headed pterodactyl which the unlucky Bumblebee soon finds he will have to attempt to ride into battle! Make sure you're not the one who ends up extinct!

Scorn:
A terrifying combination of war machine and predator, Scorn has two tricks up his sleeves (or would do if he had any sleeves): he wields the deadly Scrapmaker sword but can also change into a lethal Spinosaurus earning him the nickname "Spike".

Slog:
A giant beast with a history rooted deep in the annals of Cybertron's past, Slog changes into a robotic Apatosaurus. Watching him in combat is truly an awesome spectacle to behold.

Snarl:
Snarl changes into a Stegosaurus, traditionally a non-meat eater and one of the more peaceful dinosaurs. But don't be fooled! Snarl is as dangerous as anyone else in the Dinobots: just be glad he is on your side!

Slug:
Very angry indeed, Slug is a powerful force but also very difficult to control, whether in robot or triceratops mode. Three horns spell trouble for anyone who gets in his way!

LOCKDOWN

The important thing to remember about Lockdown is that unlike most Transformers, he has no loyalty to anyone. Neither Decepticon nor Autobot, Lockdown is a bounty hunter and will serve literally anyone who will pay him enough…even if this means treachery and betrayal. And Lockdown doesn't come alone: his impressive prison ship is packed with convicts, many of whom make up the worst collection of villainy in the known universe. And though he might think otherwise, Lockdown isn't much better himself. Switching into a Lamborghini, he's just as evil as the Decepticons.

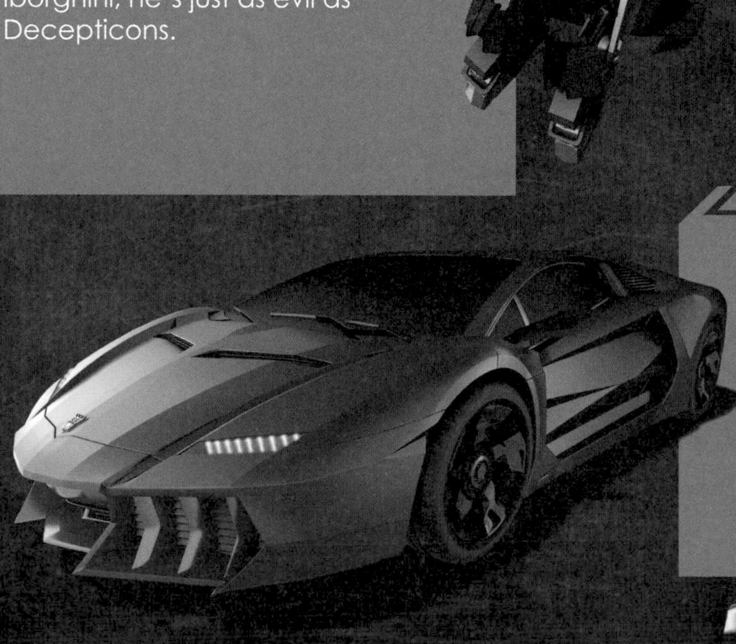

AFFILIATION: NONE
JOB TITLE: BOUNTY HUNTER
ALT MODE: LAMBORGHINI
PRIMARY WEAPON: SWORD ARM

IN SUMMARY : Cunning, two-faced and unprincipled, he'll either be your best friend or worst enemy…provided the price is right!

GRIMLOCK

Fearsome and formidable, Grimlock and the other Dinobots' origins are unclear. Optimus Prime found him imprisoned on Lockdown's prison ship. More than twice the size of the Autobots and with a lethal alternative dinosaur mode, Prime's certainly very glad he's on his side! Grimlock is just as dangerous as the original dinosaurs who became extinct 65 million years ago.

AFFILIATION: DINOBOT
JOB TITLE: LEADER
ALT MODE: TYRANNOSAURUS REX
PRIMARY WEAPON: HIS JAWS

IN SUMMARY: Not the cleverest Transformer in the world...but don't let him hear you say that!

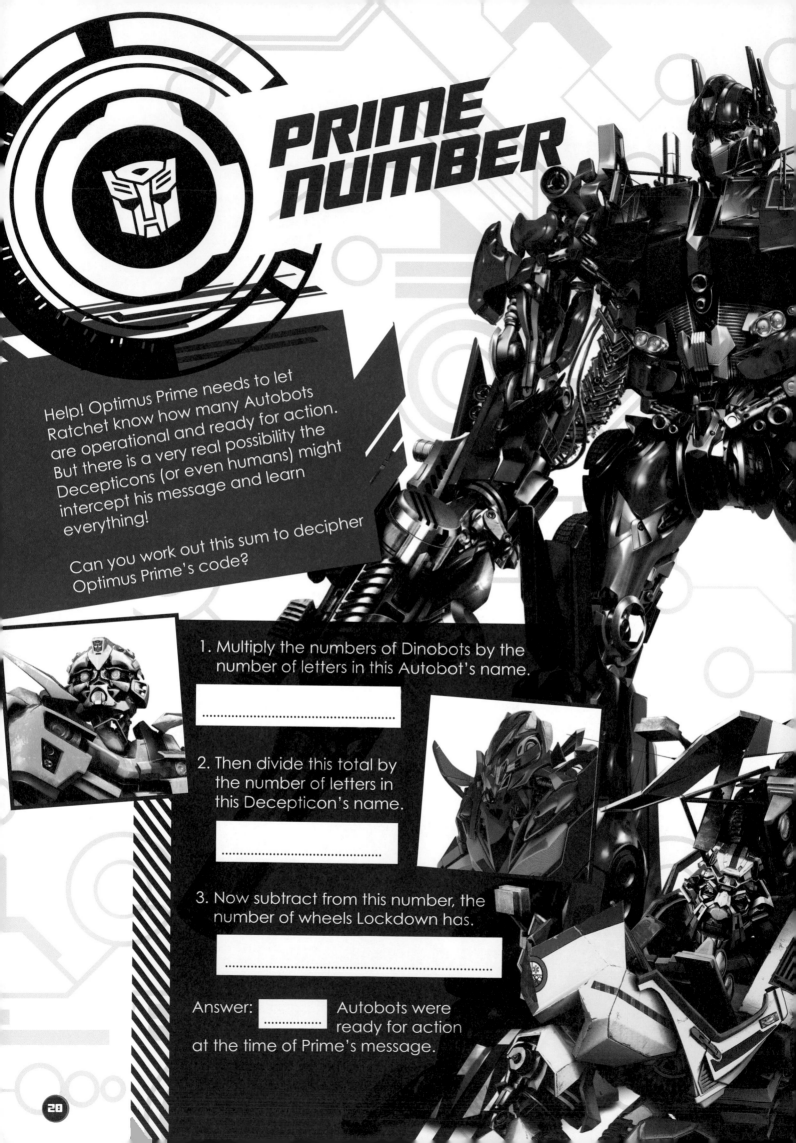

PRIME NUMBER

Help! Optimus Prime needs to let Ratchet know how many Autobots are operational and ready for action. But there is a very real possibility the Decepticons (or even humans) might intercept his message and learn everything!

Can you work out this sum to decipher Optimus Prime's code?

1. Multiply the numbers of Dinobots by the number of letters in this Autobot's name.

....

2. Then divide this total by the number of letters in this Decepticon's name.

....

3. Now subtract from this number, the number of wheels Lockdown has.

....

Answer: [   ] Autobots were
.... ready for action
at the time of Prime's message.

AGE OF EXTINCTION

Age of Extinction: three words that spell huge trouble for the Autobots, the Yeager family and quite possibly, the future of all life on Earth! But look at the words themselves: how many smaller words can you find? There are 15 letters there and we won't allow the words AGE, OF or EXTINCTION to be included!

How many can you find? Use a pen or pencil to write in your answers below. wGive yourself two points for every word you get which is five letters or longer in length!

Good luck!

cage

How did you do?

0-10 words: Ho hum! Not too bad!

11-20 words: That's more like it!

20 or more: Awesome!

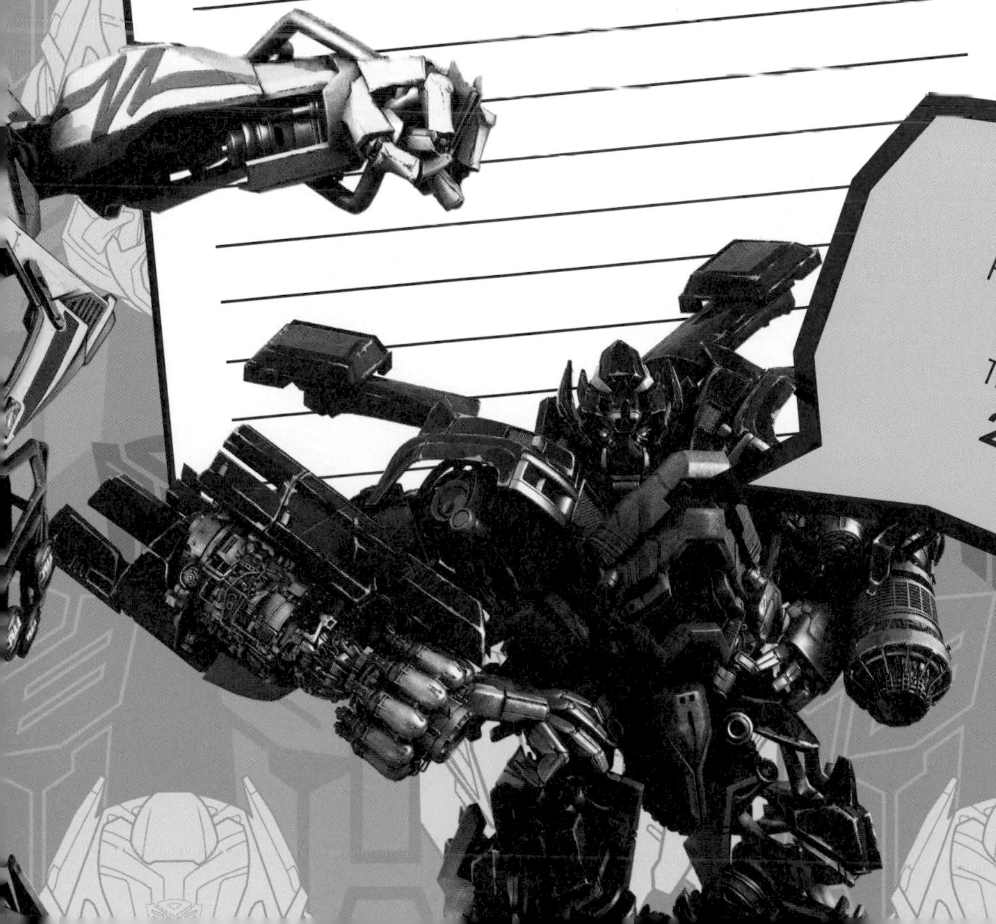

LOCKDOWN'S LOWDOWN...

Lockdown, the Decepticon, has been captured and the Autobots are questioning him to discover all they can about the Decepticons' plans. But how can anyone be sure if he is telling the truth about anything? Take a look at these statements he has made. How many are true and how many are false?

1. Optimus Prime is the leader of all the Transformers.

TRUE ☐
FALSE ☐

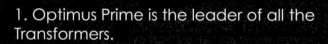

TRUE ☐
FALSE ☐

2. The Autobot Drift used to be a Decepticon.

3. Galvatron is a Decepticon.

TRUE ☐
FALSE ☐

TRUE ☐
FALSE ☐

4. The Transformers were first created by a robot called Cybertron.

5. Ratchet is the Autobots' medical officer.

TRUE ☐
FALSE ☐

TRUE ☐
FALSE ☐

6. The Dinobots are now extinct

7. The Autobots have been in contact with the humans Cade and Tessa Yeager.

TRUE ☐
FALSE ☐

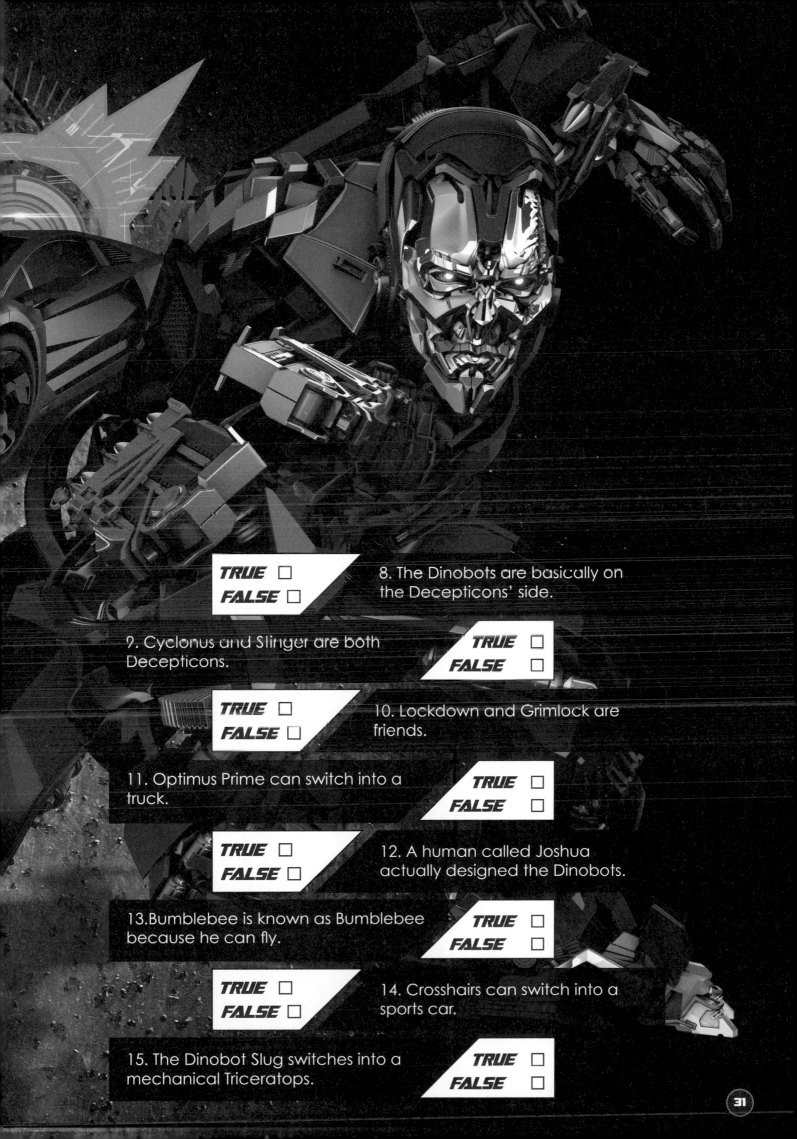

TRUE ☐
FALSE ☐

8. The Dinobots are basically on the Decepticons' side.

9. Cyclonus and Slinger are both Decepticons.

TRUE ☐
FALSE ☐

TRUE ☐
FALSE ☐

10. Lockdown and Grimlock are friends.

11. Optimus Prime can switch into a truck.

TRUE ☐
FALSE ☐

TRUE ☐
FALSE ☐

12. A human called Joshua actually designed the Dinobots.

13. Bumblebee is known as Bumblebee because he can fly.

TRUE ☐
FALSE ☐

TRUE ☐
FALSE ☐

14. Crosshairs can switch into a sports car.

15. The Dinobot Slug switches into a mechanical Triceratops.

TRUE ☐
FALSE ☐

BOTROBS IN GISSUIDE

In a desperate bid to spread chaos and confuse the Autobots, the Decepticons have scrambled the names of some of the Transformers. Can you unscramble these tricky anagrams?

Be warned! The Decepticons may even of mixed up their own names in an effort to maximise confusion!

Watch Out!

Cold wonk
....

Resting
....

Pure optimism
....

Oval grant
....

Chatter
....

Or cars hiss
....

Duh no
....

Mock Girl
....

FRIEND OR FOE?

Ratchet's night vision has failed! Help him to identify these transformers by their silhouettes alone...

1

2

3

4

WHO iS WHO?

Bumblebee: _____

Megatron: _____

Optimus Prime: _____

Ironhide: _____

SHOCKWAVE'S Shock and Awe! 1

I am Shockwave, the greatest Decepticon of them all! Dare any of you puny humans attempt to take me on and defeat me in my two quiz challenges? Make a note of your final score at the end of this test and then add it to your total for the second set of Shockwave's Shock and Awe later in the Annual! Be warned: YOU WILL FAIL!

1 Which of these is NOT one of the Dinobots?

a) Grimlock ☐
b) Scrape ☐
c) Swoop ☐

2 The human Cade Yeager works as what...?

a) An Inventor ☐
b) A Mechanic ☐
c) A Doctor ☐

3 What is the name of Cade's daughter?

a) Tessa ☐
b) Tara ☐
c) Tammy ☐

4 Grimlock, the Dinobot leader, changes into a robotic version of what...?

a) A stegosaurus ☐
b) A brontosaurus ☐
c) A Tyrannosaurus Rex ☐

5 The character Joshua longs to do what...?

a) Kill all the Transformers ☐
b) Build his own Transformers ☐
c) Become a Transformer himself ☐

6 Joshua's young geologist assistant is called what...?

a) Duffy ☐
b) Daisy ☐
c) Darcy ☐

7 Galvatron was created by...?

a) Like the others, he comes from Cybertron ☐
b) He was created by humans ☐
c) The Autobots made him by mistake ☐

8 The Dinobots are, of course, modelled on dinosaurs. But (roughly) when did dinosaurs cease to live on Earth?

a) 65 million years ago ☐
b) 50 million years ago ☐
c) Wednesday November 12th 2013, just after afternoon tea ☐

9

How, according to the Age of Extinction, did the dinosaurs die out?

a) A meteorite hit the Earth creating a dust cloud which blotted out all sunlight ☐
b) The Decepticons killed them ☐
c) The Earth was metallised ☐

10

Which organisation is Harold Attinger the head of …?

a) The CIA ☐
b) The Decepticons ☐
c) The Savoy strike team ☐

11

What is the name of Cade's best friend?

a) Lucas ☐
b) Lloyd ☐
c) Larry ☐

12

Which of these characters does NOT appear in Transformers Age of Extinction?

a) Phoenix ☐
b) Stinger ☐
c) Grimlock ☐

13

How many Dinobots are there?

a) Three ☐
b) Four ☐
c) Five ☐

14

The Dinobots are modelled on prehistoric monsters, namely, dinosaurs. But what is the meaning of the word "dino-saur"?

a) Extinct animals ☐
b) Terrible lizards ☐
c) Scary monsters ☐

15

What can the new protoypes do, which the original Transformers cannot?

a) Hypo-evolve ☐
b) Fly ☐
c) Time travel ☐

Remember puny human! Keep hold of your doubtless pathetic score for we shall meet again for more questioning later!

RATCHET'S RIDDLES

Ratchet loves a good riddle as much as the next armoured robot warrior. Use these clues to work out which Transformers he is talking about...

1. He may seem sweet as honey, but there's always lots of buzz around him.

....

2. His name might suggest he's a gloomy character but he keeps a closed door on such feelings.

....

3. He's got you in his sights.

....

4. It's a dog's life being this Transformer.

....

5. Watch out! Like a wasp or a jellyfish. Or a prickly nettle.

....

6. Top of the Autobots.

....

7. He changes into a Lamborghini.

....

8. Two heads are better than one for this Dinobot!

....

9. Guaranteed to float in and out of trouble.

....

10. The spirit of Megatron lives on in this one!

....

1
START

2

3
You chance across a stray oil barrel. Roll again as the fuel gives you extra energy.

4

5

6
Enemy patrol ahead! Miss a tur while you change and disguise yourself.

23

22

21

20

19
Decepticon booby trap! Go back to the start!

18

24

26
Galvatron ambushes you! Go back six spaces.

25

27

28

29

30

31

32

PRIME TIME

7

8 →

9

10 →

11

12

Sneak attack by Stinger ! Go back four spaces.

Optimus Prime has been captured! Can you and your friends rescue him before it's too late? Get a dice, grab some friends and get going! The first one to the final square wins and will be officially a Friend of the Autobots forever. Good luck!

16

The Dinobots join youl Go forward five spaces.

15

14 ←

13

17

37

38 →

39

40 **FINISH**

Well done! You have rescued Optimus Prime!

36 ↑

33

ou are fooled y a Decepticon ecoy! Go back ur spaces.

34 →

35

CLASH OF THE TITANS!

Colour in this exciting action scene using whatever colours you like!

BUMBLE BEE

Maybe it's because he's smaller than the average Transformer. Or maybe it's because he has spent more time in the company of humans than most. Or maybe there's just something human in Bumblebee's nature. Whatever it is, Bumblebee is often seen as the most human of all the Transformers.

This apparent softness is misleading though. With two plasma cannons, Bumblebee can certainly hold his own in a combat situation. Many Decepticons have underestimated Bumblebee in the past and perished as a result. As someone once said (about someone else), he may float like a butterfly, but he stings like a bee.

AFFILIATION: AUTOBOT
JOB TITLE: ACTING LEADER
ALT MODE: SPORTS CAR

In summary: Not the biggest or the strongest Autobot but certainly one of the most loyal.

PRIME OBJECTIVE

Optimus Prime is lost: separated from his fellow Autobots at the height of a major battle with the evil Decepticons. Can you transport the Autobot leader through this maze and away from the Decepticons so that he can resume command as quickly as possible?

START

FINISH

TRANSFORMERS
THE DARK OF THE MOON

The Earth's moon, 1969, and the first ever men to land on the moon, Neil Armstrong and Edwin "Buzz" Aldrin make a startling discovery: wreckage from a crashed alien space ship on the moon's surface. Clearly, mankind will no longer be alone in the universe. In fact, the ship is The Ark, once piloted by Sentinel Prime whose large robotic body still lies inactive within the craft. Fleeing from Cybertron with some new hugely advanced technology of his own invention on board, Sentinel Prime had crash landed on the moon many years before.

Forty years later and three years after the events of Revenge of The Fallen, the Autobots, who are still part of the military unit NEST, have by now become actively involved in helping the people of Earth with their own problems. While assisting in making an old Russian nuclear power station safe again, Optimus Prime learns for the first time about the crashed ship on the moon. Travelling there himself, Optimus revives Sentinel Prime using a special device called the Matrix of Leadership. He also brings four pillars from the space bridge and a control pillar from Sentinel Prime's highly advanced ship back to Earth.

Meanwhile, Sam Witwicky has learned of a Decepticon conspiracy and is able to warn the Autobots that the Decepticons had known Sentinel Prime was on the moon all along. Could Sentinel Prime be about to face some sort of attack from the Decepticons?

'If we just do what they want, how are we ever going to live with ourselves?'

45

'You're lucky I didn't kill you. In time you'll see!'

But all is not as it seems. Sentinel Prime reveals he has in fact done a deal with Megatron! He had become convinced that the Autobots can never win the war against the Decepticons. He proceeds to open a space bridge, creating a portal enabling an army of Decepticons hidden under the moon's surface to attack the Earth.

Sentinel Prime convinces the human governments of Earth to persuade the Autobots to leave the Earth forever. The Autobots leave aboard a craft called the Xantium and Optimus Prime sadly concludes that the humans really are on their own from now on. Suddenly the ship comes under attack, then: disaster! The Decepticon Starscream destroys the Xantium! Is this the end for the Autobots?

With the Autobots gone, the Decepticons run riot on Earth, destroying most of the city of Chicago and setting up a pillar for the space bridge inside the city. The Decepticon plan is not to return to their home world but instead to bring Cybertron into Earth's orbit and force Earth's population of six billion humans into becoming slaves for their new Decepticon masters.

Fortunately, on his way to Chicago, Sam discovers that the Autobots had not been killed after all! In fact they never intended to leave Earth and escaped in a rocket booster that blasted off the Xantium, just before Starscream's attack.

Soon, Sam accompanied by members of NEST, as well as the Autobots, are able to rescue Sam's new girlfriend Carly, who had been captured by the Decepticons. A major battle begins. Sam is able to kill Starscream while Optimus kills a fiendish Decepticon known as the Driller, who has a knack for bringing down skyscrapers. Bumblebee meanwhile, kills top Decepticon spy Soundwave, while Optimus is able to finish off the leading Decepticon Shockwave. He then uses Shockwave's own arm cannon to destroy the space bridge's control pillar, deactivating the bridge. Clearly the tide is turning in the Autobots' favour. But the battle is not over yet - Optimus Prime is locked in combat with Sentinel Prime, and Sentinel at first seems to be winning.

Convinced that he would never be able to rule Cybertron alone with Sentinel Prime alive, Megatron surprisingly attacks the traitor Sentinel, guaranteeing Sentinel's defeat. Meanwhile, in the heat of battle, Bumblebee destroys the pillar for good, destroying the space bridge and bringing an end to the Transformers' home world of Cybertron in the process.

'We will kill them all!'

Recognising his defeat, Megatron offers Optimus Prime a truce. He wants to remain in charge of the Decepticon forces, but Optimus refuses to accept the Decepticon's terms. Spitefully, Megatron attempts to shoot Optimus, but fails and Optimus fights back and finally kills him with an axe. The traitor Sentinel Prime is also killed soon after. Peace is restored once again and Sam and his girlfriend Carly are reunited. The Autobots are forced to confront a harsh truth: their home world Cybertron is probably gone forever. However, they can now accept Earth as their new home.

SHOCKWAVE'S Shock and Awe! 2

So puny human fools! Don't you know when you are beaten? I see you have come crawling back for more punishment. Can you attempt these questions based around events BEFORE the Age of Extinction. Hopefully, some of you will have at least remembered to keep a note of your results from the earlier quiz and be able to add them to your score for this one.

1 Bumblebee changes into what...?

a) A car ☐
b) A boat ☐
c) A giant bee ☐

2 Which of these is NOT a Transformers film?

a) The Revenge of the Fallen ☐
b) The Edge of Eternity ☐
c) The Dark of the Moon ☐

3 Galvatron is not in the first three Transformer films. Who led the Decepticons before him?

a) Megatron ☐
b) Devastator ☐
c) Starscream ☐

4 What exactly was the AllSpark?

a) A sacred fabled object which has the power to generate new Transformer life ☐
b) The Transformers' home planet ☐
c) The name of the Autobot HQ on Earth ☐

5 Which of these is the name of an Autobot?

a) Rock ☐
b) Jazz ☐
c) Grunge ☐

6 The human, who helps the Autobots in the first three films, was called...?

a) Joe Albuquerque ☐
b) Sam Witwicky ☐
c) Max Capacity ☐

7 What is NEST?

a) Optimus Prime's personal computer ☐
b) A secret anti-Decepticon military unit ☐
c) Bumblebee's holiday cottage ☐

8 Who was the oldest Autobot?

a) Optimus Prime ☐
b) Ratchet ☐
c) Ironhide ☐

9 Which of these first appears in Dark of the Moon?

a) Septimus Prime ☐
b) Optimus Prime ☐
c) Sentinel Prime ☐

10 In the same film, who discovers Transformers on the moon?

a) Astronauts on the historic Apollo 11 mission ☐
b) Scientists looking at the moon through a telescope ☐
c) A visiting party of aliens from Neptune ☐

11 In what ship did Sentinel Prime escape from Cybertron?

a) The Prime Mover ☐
b) The Ark ☐
c) The Battleship Cybertron ☐

12 What was the aim of The Fallen?

a) To turn the Star Harvester onto our sun and destroy it ☐
b) To turn the human race into Decepticons ☐
c) To kidnap Bumblebee ☐

13 What is Ratchet's absolute Number One priority?

a) Preserving and saving as many lives as possible
b) Preserving and saving us many Autobot lives as possible
c) Winning the war

14 In the first film, which Transformer did Sam meet first?

a) Optimus Prime
b) Shockwave
c) Bumblebee

15 And finally, why are the Autobots and Decepticons fighting?

a) No one knows ☐
b) They just like fighting ☐
c) The Decepticons secretly want Optimus Prime to be their leader ☐

So how did you do?

0-10: Absolutely pathetic! You are hopelessly ignorant. Perhaps you should consider joining the Dinobots?

11-20: Hmmm. About what I would expect from a simple carbon based life form such as yourself. Give yourself a pat on the back. But only one, mind! You're not that clever.

21-30: I'm impressed human! To be honest, I didn't even score that much myself and I wrote the quiz! You win…this time!

WHICH TRANSFORMER ARE YOU?

Fortunately, as humans, we are not usually forced to take sides in the ongoing Autobots vs. Decepticons battle. But what if we were? Answer the following questions and then look at the summary on the opposing page to discover whether your personality is closest to that of the Autobots or to that of the Decepticons.

A party is being held and everyone at school seems to have been invited except you. How do you respond?

a) Rise above it. It's only a party. You know you'll find other things to do instead.
b) Drop "subtle" hints to the person hosting the party in case you've been forgotten.
c) Organise a rival party of your own on the same night. Sabotage the invites to the other party to ensure that anyone planning to go ends up at your address instead. Make doubly sure, by using your network of spies to burst all the balloons at the other party and to steal any birthday cake.

Class is about to begin in an hour when you realise that you've totally forgotten to prepare for today's big History test. You are not even sure what it's on. Do you…?

a) Go to the school mega-early and attempt to memorise all aspects of human history on the off chance some of it comes up.
b) Perhaps mention to your teacher that you forgot but try your best to complete the test anyway.
c) Deliberately sprain your own ankle on the way to school and then use your subsequent day off to swot up on the test you'll have to do on your return anyway.

It is your grandmother's birthday and she is sick with a cold. Do you…?

a) Travel the forty miles to her house on foot through heavy rain to deliver her present in person.
b) Post her a card and order something nice online before phoning her to check she's alright that evening.
c) Do nothing. Who cares about anyone else?

What is your main goal in life?

a) To devote yourself to the preservation of humanity. To provide leadership and freedom to the world.
b) To get through life in as enjoyable, interesting and trouble-free fashion as possible.
c) World domination.

Your friend is coming over and suggests bringing a DVD or Blu-ray. In addition to one of the Transformers films (obviously) what sort of film do you recommend he or she brings?

a) Something inspirational about someone who has dramatically improved the world. ☐
b) Dunno. Some sort of action or comedy. Whatever. ☐
c) A war film. Or anything where the baddies win. ☐

Who are your role models?

a) Great leaders. Thinkers, Statesmen and women. ☐
b) Great sportsmen. Actors and actresses. Music stars. ☐
c) Dictators. Gangsters. Criminals. ☐

Which of these qualities is the most important?

a) A desire to improve society ☐
b) A sense of humour ☐
c) Strength and the ability to achieve as much power as possible. ☐

What were your favourite books as a child?

a) Inspirational and awe inspiring biographies. ☐
b) Harry Potter. ☐
c) Horror. Anything violent. ☐

Which superpower would you most like to have?

a) The ability to metamorphose into a car or van. ☐
b) Invisibility or perhaps time travel. ☐
c) Transformation powers. Plus the ability to bend and manipulate people to your will. ☐

Your results...

Mostly As: Wow! You are as high minded and wise as Optimus Prime himself. Hang on! Are you sure you are not actually Optimus Prime? Seriously, you seem very nice and everything but you might want to lighten up a bit.

Mostly Bs: You are neither an Autobot or a Decepticon. Which, for a human, is fairly normal.

Mostly Cs: Yikes! You clearly have Decepticon tendencies. You are an evil, despicable fiend. Indeed, you've probably found some sneaky way to cheat in this test and are even now reading the "Mostly As" bit. Be gone!

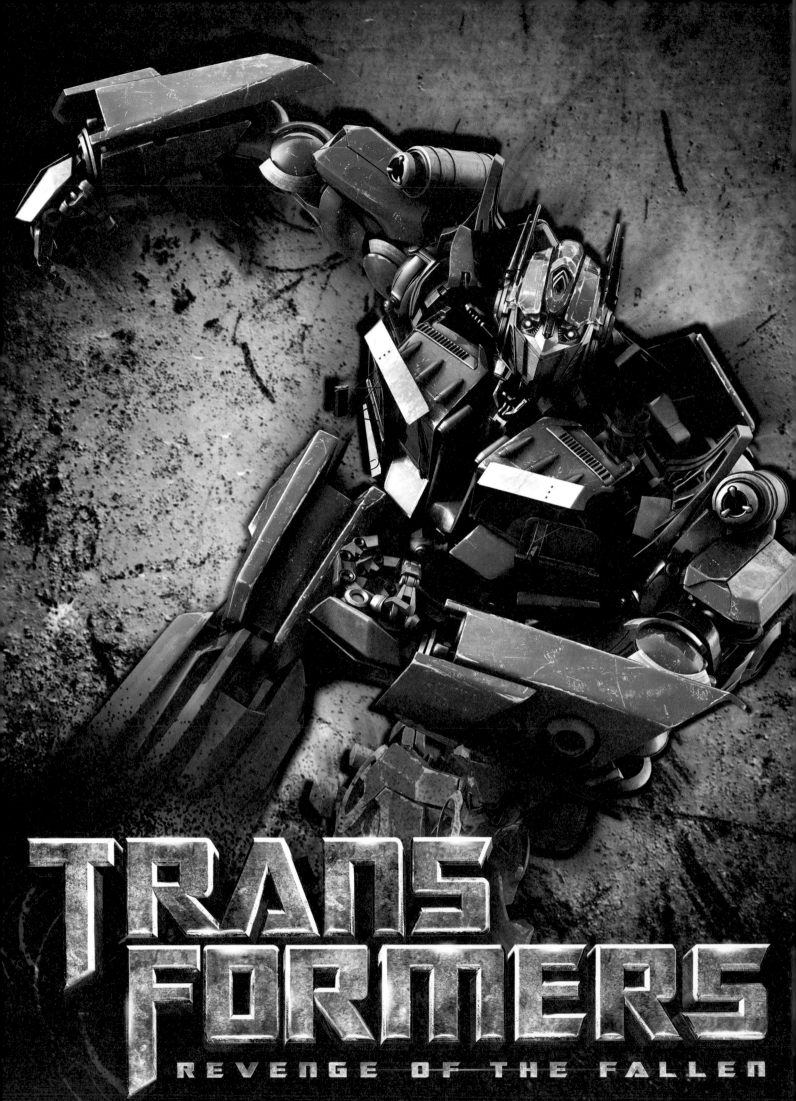

RATCHET REBOOTS!

As medical officer for the Autobots, Ratchet needs exactly the right spare parts to repair whichever Transformer he needs. Look at the following spare parts labelled A to E. Can you locate them within the larger picture below? Circle your answers with a pen or pencil.

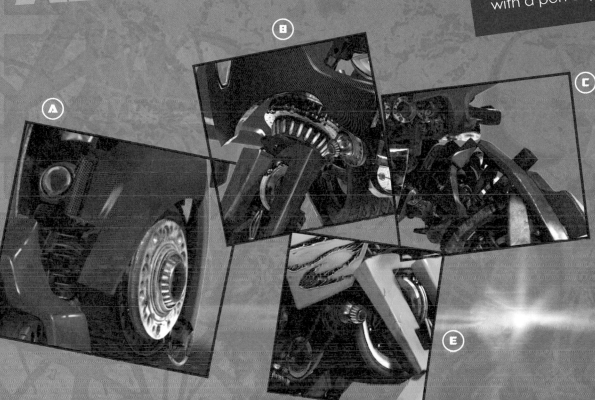

A

B

C

D

E

Megatron's Masterplan

What is the Decepticon leader up to now? Crack this clever code to decipher the message sent by Megatron to all Decepticons which Ratchet intercepted.

A B C D E F G H I J K L M

N O P Q R S T U V W X Y Z

REAL OR FAKE?

Megatron has asked Starscream for a list of Transformers names past and present. This message has now been intercepted by the Autobots. Can you help Ironhide sort out the real names from the fake ones, which Starscream made up.

REAL FAKE	**Ironclad**	**Sentinel Prime**	REAL FAKE
REAL FAKE	**Mudflap**	**Silverfish**	REAL FAKE
REAL FAKE	**Ladybird**	**The Fallen**	REAL FAKE
REAL FAKE	**Thunderclaw**	**Jazz**	REAL FAKE
REAL FAKE	**Warpath**	**Battleghost**	REAL FAKE

TRANSFORMERS
REVENGE OF THE FALLEN

Two years have passed. The Autobots have found a new home with NEST, a group of soldiers dedicated to hunting down and destroying all remaining Decepticons. On one such mission in Shanghai, Optimus Prime and the elderly Autobot Ironhide kill one such: Demolishor. But just as they are finishing him off, the stricken Decepticon utters a mysterious final sentence: "The Fallen shall rise again!" The Autobots are baffled. What could this mean?

Sam Witwicky is doing his best to forget about the battles of two years before. He is preparing for college when suddenly he finds a splinter of the lost AllSpark in an old t-shirt. It is a small splinter but it has a huge effect, flooding Sam's brain with images, burning his hand, bringing kitchen appliances in the house to life and setting fire to the house. Thankfully, the house survives but Sam's mother is very angry with both Sam and Bumblebee. Sam gives the splinter of AllSpark to his girlfriend Mikaela before he leaves for college. Bumblebee leaves to rejoin his old Autobot friends.

Unfortunately, nobody notices what appears to be a small toy car on a nearby lawn. In fact, it is a Decepticon spy which promptly passes on news of the existence of the AllSpark splinter to the Decepticon Soundwave who is orbiting the Earth, disguised as a satellite. Soundwave goes on to pick up more information, also eavesdropping on a conversation between Optimus Prime and an American general. During this chat, Prime reveals the existence of an AllSpark shard which he retrieved following the destruction of Megatron and the fact that Megatron's remains are located in the Laurentian Abyss, an especially deep part of the ocean close to Canada. The general doesn't like Prime, however, blaming the Autobots for the Decepticons' interest in Earth in the first place. But now Soundwave is able to tell the

Decepticon Ravage where the shard is. Ravage is able to steal the shard from the NEST base.

On hearing this news, the Autobots decide Sam is the person to help them. Bumblebee takes a reluctant Sam away from a college party to meet Optimus Prime, who asks for him to speak to the American government and generals on his behalf.

Before long, Ravage is able to travel to the Abyss. With the aid of some Constructicons, he is soon able to revive the fallen Decepticon leader. Having returned to life, Megatron wastes no time at all. Crushing an attempt to overthrow him by his old rival Starscream, Megatron presents himself before his new master, The Fallen. The Fallen is the founder of all the Decepticons. The Fallen reveals that when the Cube was destroyed, the knowledge within the AllSpark transferred to Sam Witwicky. The Fallen orders Megatron to defeat Optimus Prime, the greatest threat to The Fallen's power and to capture Sam.

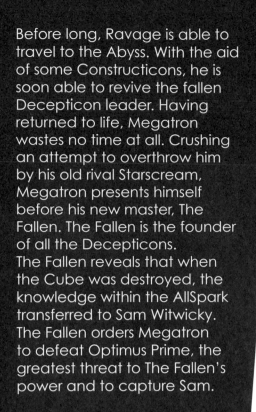

'Let's ROLL'
– OPTIMUS PRIME

Megatron, Starscream and another Decepticon, Grindor, manage to kidnap Sam and try to remove his brain. A fight ensues between Prime and Megatron, when the Autobot leader enters a nearby forest in an attempt to rescue Sam. Ripping Grindor's head to pieces, Optimus seems set to kill Megatron. But shockingly, Megatron stabs Optimus Prime as Sam and his friends retreat into the forest to escape.

Prime's lifeless body falls to the ground. He is dead!

Delighted by Prime's death, The Fallen uses all the communications in the world to make a deal with humanity: give me Sam Witwicky and I will let the human race survive. Sam has no choice other than to go on the run.

'Now, I claim your son'

– THE FALLEN

But Sam is not alone. He, Mikaela and Bumblebee meet an ex-Sector Seven agent Seymour Simmons who reveals to them that the Transformers first visited the Earth in ancient Egyptian times. The group are then teleported to modern day Egypt by an old Autobot Jetfire who used to be a Decepticon. Jetfire explains how Optimus Prime could yet be brought back to life if they can take him to the mystical Tomb of Primes there. NEST set about bringing Prime's boy to Egypt, along with the other Autobots.

The tomb is soon found. But the Decepticons have now kidnapped Sam's parents in an attempt to get to Sam. Thankfully, Bumblebee rescues the older Witwickys, killing the Decepticons Rampage and Ravage as he does so. The Decepticons then launch an attack, demolishing one of the ancient pyramids and revealing the Sun Harvester, an ancient Decepticon machine that would destroy the sun, which was hidden underneath. Sam is shot and badly wounded by Megatron but thankfully the Autobots are able to rescue him. They also restore the mystical Matrix of Leadership and using that, bring Optimus Prime back to life.

The Fallen now arrives, stealing the Matrix to start the Star Harvester. But now Optimus Prime has taken new parts from the dying Jetfire and uses these new powers to destroy the Sun Harvester and battle both Megatron and The Fallen, knocking them off a pyramid. Soon the Fallen is dead as Prime brutally tears out his life spark by ripping his arm through the first Decepticon's chest.

Victory has been won. Megatron and Starscream escape while the Autobots and humans return to the United States.

FIGHT TO THE DEATH!

The sight of Transformers in combat is scary enough even when they are in black and white. Bring this scene to life by colouring it in…

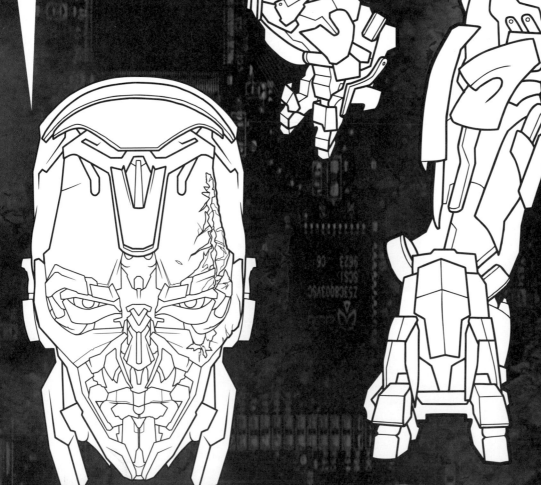

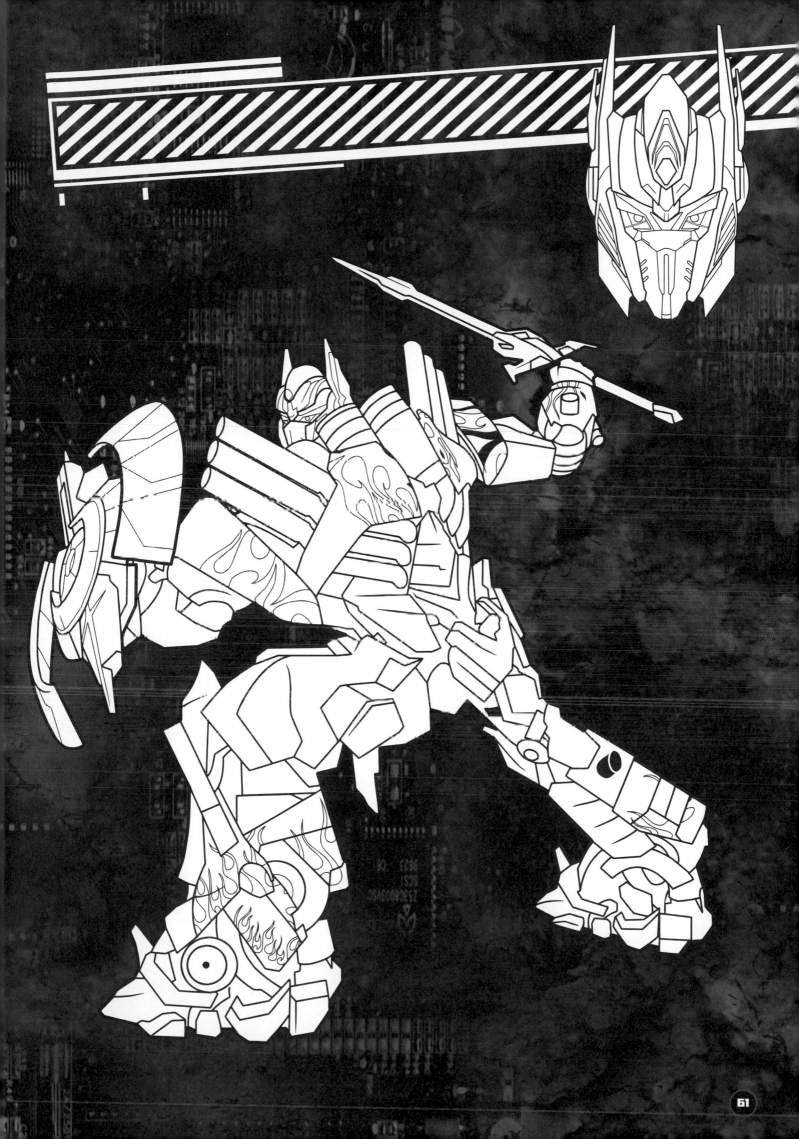

TRANSFORM YOURSELF

Ever wanted to be a Transformer? Well, now's your chance with these Autobot and Decepticon face masks!

You will need:
1. A pair of scissors.
2. Some string or elastic.
3. Some glue and sticky tape.
4. Some card.

Remember scissors are sharp. Ask an adult for help before using.

ARRIVAL FROM CYBERTRON...

Long ago, in the furthest reaches of space, the planet Cybertron is home to a terrible war between two groups of robots. On one side are the Autobots: brave, noble, heroic. The other: the evil Decepticons, led by Megatron, a hate-filled being dedicated to gaining control of the AllSpark, a mystical object thought to be the source of all life on the planet.

In his desperation to gain control of the object, Megatron crash lands on a remote planet, Earth. The impact of the crash ends up with both Megatron and the AllSpark, frozen between the surface of the Arctic. There they remained for a long long time...

Much later, in the 19th century, Arctic explorer Archibald Witwicky makes an incredible discovery. A giant robot frozen in the snow! While examining this new discovery, Archibald accidentally activates Megatron's malfunctioning navigation system and the exact details of Megatron's location are imprinted on the explorer's glasses. Soon after, the AllSpark is found too and, recognising its power, the American government builds the famous Hoover Dam around it, just to keep it hidden from view.

'JOIN THEM IN EXTINCTION!'
– MEGATRON

Many years later, ordinary teenager Sam Witwicky (the great-great grandson of the famous explorer) walks into a used car lot and chooses a car for himself. He has many things on his mind that day - particularly Mikaela, a beautiful local girl he fancies. Sam picks out a bright yellow car. But Sam hasn't chosen the car, it has chosen him! For this is no ordinary car. It is Bumblebee, a leading figure in the Autobots. Sam is totally unaware of this until one day, unexpectedly, Bumblebee starts driving off

down the street by himself. Having chased him for several blocks, Sam is amazed when Bumblebee suddenly switches into his robotic form right in front of him. The robot then begins to signal to other Autobots in space.

Meanwhile, the Decepticons, leaderless without Megatron, launch an attack on a US base in the Middle Eastern country of Qatar. Their plan is to find out exactly where Megatron is by hacking into the system. Having failed, a Decepticon called Frenzy

attempts to download the info by infiltrating the president's plane, Air Force One. But they are thwarted again, this time by Maggie Madsen, a young technician who recognises what is happening and manages to convince her bosses to shut down the entire network. However, by scanning the data Frenzy has managed to download, they uncover information on the explorer's glasses. The Decepticons immediately start to track down the location of the glasses in order to find out exactly where Megatron is.

Now it is Sam who is having his life transformed. He, Mikaela and Bumblebee become involved in a furious battle with another Decepticon Barricade. Having finally defeated Barricade in a power station, Bumblebee finally introduces himself properly to the two young humans. He then takes Sam and Mikaela to a pre-arranged meeting place where they meet more Autobots: Jazz, Ironhide, Ratchet and their leader Optimus Prime.

Still in a state of shock, Sam and Mikaela agree to help Optimus Prime. But, just as they arrive at Sam's house, agents from the US government swoop in, arrest Sam and Mikaela and capture Bumblebee himself.

Reluctantly, Optimus Prime orders the Autobots to withdraw. He then finds Archibald's old glasses in Sam's house and uses them to locate the AllSpark's location behind the Hoover Dam. He vows then and there that if the Decepticons cannot be beaten any other way, he will merge the Cube with his own spark, a process that would lead to his own destruction, but would at least defeat the Decepticons.

The Decepticons are also on the verge of locating the AllSpark and Megatron had started to thaw out. At last the government recognises the danger the world is in and releases Bumblebee, who promptly converts the AllSpark into a smaller form in order to deliver it to Optimus Prime. A convoy of Autobots, along with Sam and Mikaela, set off for Mission City.

Total war breaks out as the convoy arrives in Mission City with US air force planes swooping in to back up the Autobots. Frenzy is killed in an attempt to stop these planes getting there while his fellow Decepticon Bonecrusher is finished off by Optimus Prime. The Autobots suffer too, with Megatron killing the Autobot Jazz and Bumblebee being badly injured in combat with Starscream. Mikaela desperately steals a truck to carry Bumblebee out of danger. Wounded, Bumblebee gives the AllSpark to Sam, and helped by Ratchet and the oldest Autobot Ironhide, he begins a dangerous mission: to get the AllSpark to military headquarters.

'You are the strangest boy I have ever met'

– MIKAELA BANES

Fighting becomes fierce as the two leaders, Megatron and Optimus Prime, become involved in an epic clash of the titans. Despite pressure from Starscream and Megatron, Sam boldly shoves the AllSpark into Megatron's chest, killing the weakened Decepticon and destroying the AllSpark.

A happy ending then, although not entirely. Bumblebee gets to stay with Sam. Sam also starts going out with Mikaela, as he had always hoped. Starscream, meanwhile, escapes into space. Optimus Prime thanks Sam for his major role in saving the Autobots and Optimus Prime's own life. The Autobot leader then sends out a signal to the stars in the hope of locating any other surviving Autobots. But with the AllSpark gone, so to are the Transformers' hopes of returning to Cybertron. They will now have to make do with their new home. Our home. Earth.

'At the end of this day, one shall stand, one shall fall'

– OPTIMUS PRIME

DRAW BUMBLEBEE

Have you ever wanted to be able to draw one of the coolest Autobots? Well, now's your chance. Use this grid to accurately recreate this picture of the mighty Bumblebee in all his glory.

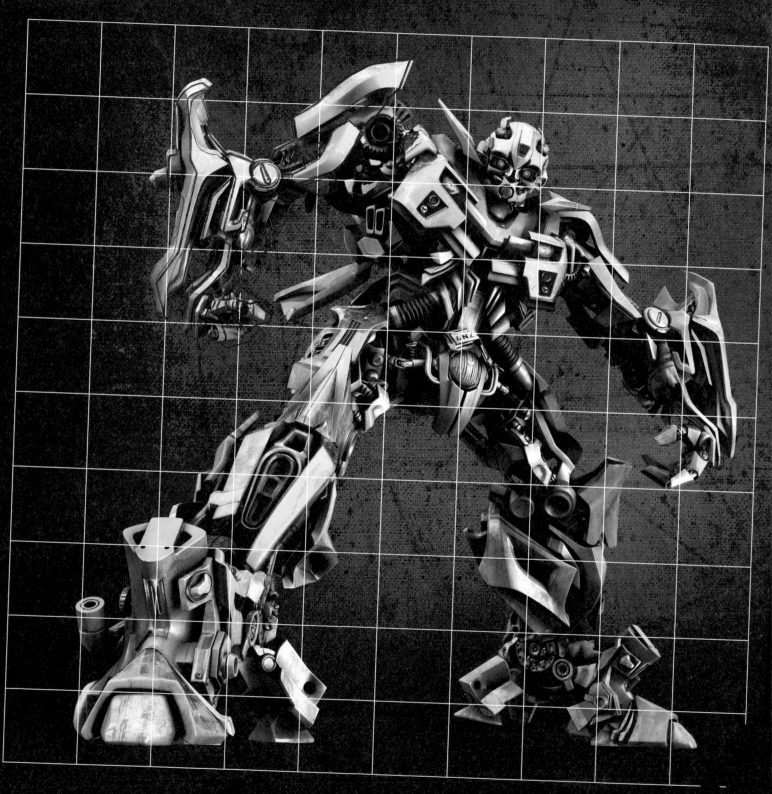

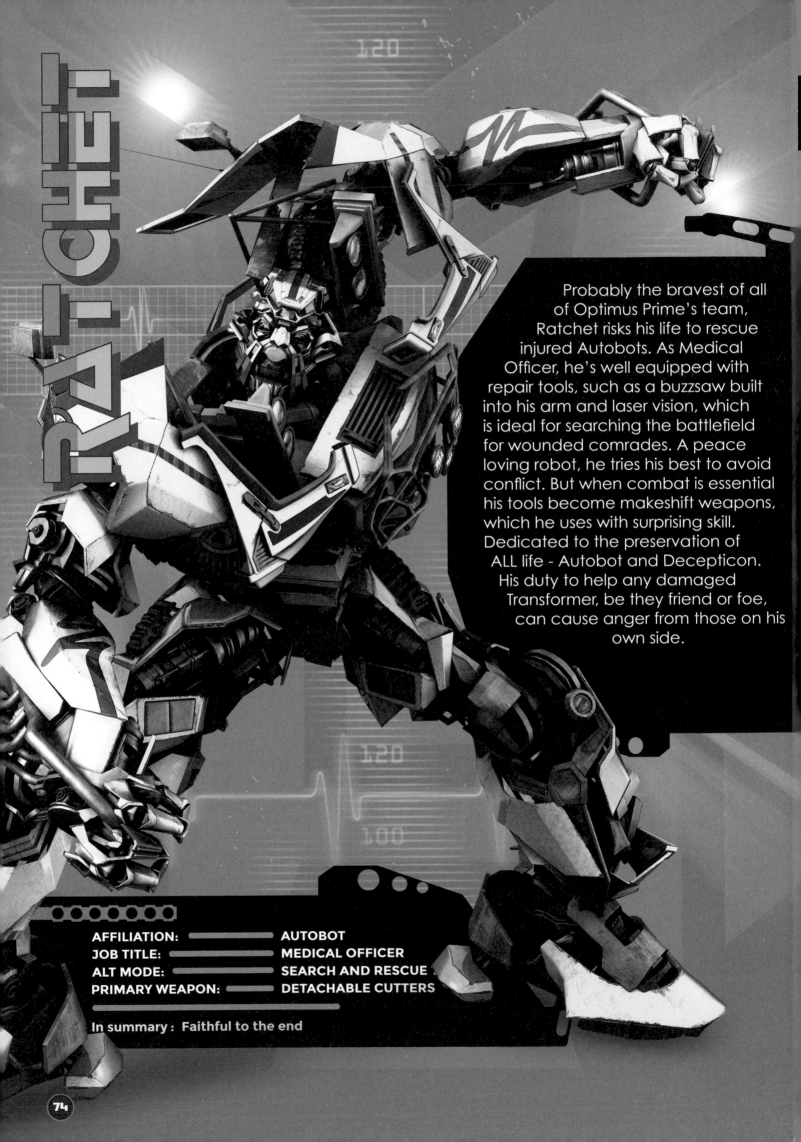

RATCHET

Probably the bravest of all of Optimus Prime's team, Ratchet risks his life to rescue injured Autobots. As Medical Officer, he's well equipped with repair tools, such as a buzzsaw built into his arm and laser vision, which is ideal for searching the battlefield for wounded comrades. A peace loving robot, he tries his best to avoid conflict. But when combat is essential his tools become makeshift weapons, which he uses with surprising skill. Dedicated to the preservation of ALL life - Autobot and Decepticon. His duty to help any damaged Transformer, be they friend or foe, can cause anger from those on his own side.

AFFILIATION: AUTOBOT
JOB TITLE: MEDICAL OFFICER
ALT MODE: SEARCH AND RESCUE
PRIMARY WEAPON: DETACHABLE CUTTERS

In summary : Faithful to the end

JOIN THE DOTS

Who on Earth is this? Do they even come FROM Earth? Join the dots to find out who it is...

ANSWERS

PAGE 11

```
Y T L A O O S M D F E C G Z
T P O B U M B L E B E E R H
T U C N J X E X C R V U V F
D T K C R O S S H A I R S Q
Z Q D C Y C L O N U S V H I
L M O G A L V A T R O N E R
V Y W V K F O H D U F V N S
G I N W M G N O I F E I R T
R R O P T I M U S P R I M E
I A L R I O P N S O V W D D
M T R E D S D D M M A R R N
L C S T I N G E R P E X I O
O H Y M R W L U A R L Q F T
C E I N I O E O B A J S T E
K T G O H I I R M V A C R T
```

PAGE 12 - 13

1 - Optimus Prime
2 - Lockdown
3 - Crosshairs
4 - Drift
5 - Bumblebee
6 - Stinger

PAGE 28

1. 7 Dinobots x 5 = 35
2. 5 ÷ 7 letters = 5
3. 5 - 4 wheels = 1

Answer:
1 Autobot was ready
for action at the time of
Prime's message

PAGE 30 - 31

1 - False
2 - True
3 - True
4 - False
5 - True
6 - False
7 - True
8 - False
9 - True
10 - False
11 - True
12 - False
13 - False
14 - True
15 - True

PAGE 32

Lockdown
Stinger
Optimus Prime
Galvatron
Ratchet
Crosshairs
Hound
Grimlock

PAGE 33

1 - Megatron
2 - Bumblebee
3 - Ironhide
4 - Optimus prime

PAGE 34 - 35

01 - B Scrape
02 - A An inventor
03 - A Tessa
04 - C Tyrannosaurus Rex
05 - B Build his own transformers
06 - C Darcy
07 - B He was created by humans
08 - A 65 million years ago
09 - C The earth was metalized
10 - C The savoy strike team
11 - A Lucas
12 - A Phoenix
13 - B Four
14 - B Terrible lizards
15 - A Hypo-evolve

PAGE 36 - 37

1 - Bumblebee   6 - Optimus Prime
2 - Grimlock   7 - Lockdown
3 - Crosshairs   8 - Strafe
4 - Hound   9 - Drift
5 - Stinger   10 - Galvatron

PAGE 43

PAGE 54

ATTENTION ALL DECEPTICONS!
CONTINUE WITH OUR PLAN TO ELIMINATE
ALL AUTOBOTS ON EARTH BEFORE MAKING
THE PUNY HUMAN POPULATION OUR SLAVES

PAGE 55

Ironclad - Fake
Mudflap - Real
Ladybird - Fake
Thunderclaw - Fake
Grimlock - Real
Sentinel Prime - Real
Silverfish   Fake
The Fallen - Real
Jazz - Real
Battleghost - Fake

PAGE 48 - 49

01 - A A Car
02 - B The Edge Of Eternity
03 - A Megatron
04 - A A Sacred Fabled Object
         Which Has The Power To
         Generate New Transformer Life
05 - B Jazz
06 - B Sam Witwicky
07 - B A Secret Anti-Decepticon
         Military Unit
08 - C Ironhide
09 - C Sentinel Prime
10 - A Astronauts On The Historic
         Apollo 11 Mission
11 - B The Ark
12 - A To Turn The Star Harvester
         Onto Our Sun And Destroy It
13 - A Preserving And Saving As Many
         Lives As Possible
14 - C Bumblebee
15 - A No one knows

PAGE 66 - 67

PAGE 75

Bumblebee

PAGE 53

E   B

A   C

Pedigree®

Visit pedigreebooks.com to discover more on the 2015 Transformers™ Annual, plus other titles in our range. Scan with your mobile device to learn more.

Pedigree Books, Beech Hill House, Walnut Gardens, Exeter EX4 4DH